First Book of
Children's
Poetry

Beaver Books

First published in 1983 by
The Hamlyn Publishing Group Limited
London · New York · Sydney · Toronto
Astronaut House, Feltham, Middlesex, England

© Copyright Cadbury Limited 1983
ISBN 0 600 20777 3

Printed and bound in Great Britain by
Cox & Wyman Limited, Reading
Set in Souvenir

Cadbury Limited and the Publishers have taken every possible precaution to ensure that the material in this book is the original work of the named writers and does not infringe the copyright of any person or body. Each poem has been authenticated by a responsible adult and the work has been carefully checked by independent experts for plagiarism. If despite this we have inadvertently failed to identify any borrowed poem we would be grateful if this could be brought to our attention for correction at the first opportunity.

Contents

Publisher's note

The poems in this book were chosen by a panel of poets, teachers and educationalists from over 34 000 entries for the Cadbury's National Exhibition of Children's Art 1983/84. This year is the first in which there has been a poetry section and the judges – Joan Freeman, educational psychologist; Jack Dalglish, Staff Inspector of English and poet; Vernon Scannell, poet; and chairman Dr Harold Riley – were delighted at the range and variety of material. They chose as outstanding the work of Mark Berry and Sarah Lucy Davies, whose poems appear on pages 80, 119, 137 and 39, 76 respectively.

Londoner Mark Berry, who was seventeen when he wrote the winning poem, has been writing poetry for six years. He will be going to university in the autumn and wants to be a writer and journalist. Sarah Lucy Davies, who is fifteen and lives in Merseyside, also intends to be a journalist. She has been writing since she was six years old and has won several national poetry prizes in competitions sponsored by *The Times Educational Supplement*, *The Observer* and W. H. Smith, as well as winning the senior section of the National Poetry Society's Children's Competition in 1982.

The judges also commended highly thirty-three children whose poems appear on pages 16, 22, 29, 38, 48, 49, 50, 58, 65, 71, 78, 81, 100, 103, 113, 115, 121, 122, 126, 128, 130, 132, 139, 142, 143, 146, 149, 150, 151, 152 and 155.

The poems have been arranged under subjects which gives the reader the opportunity to compare the ideas of children from as young as four to mature seventeen-year-olds. All the illustrations are taken from entries to the Art and Craft side of this year's Exhibition, and they complement the poems in an unusual and satisfying way.

The judges were interested to see how children's writing develops, from the artless spontaneity of the very youngest, such as Jason Upham's 'The Flowers What Grow So High' (page 6), through a period when the writers are strongly influenced by their reading, to the mature work of the older writers who have found their own 'voice'. A good example of the way in which budding poets use 'real' poems as a springboard is Susan Mantle's 'The Sea' (page 91) in which the writer uses James Reeves's theme from his poem 'The Sea' in *The Wandering Moon* (published by Heinemann) and develops her own ideas from this image.

We are very pleased to be publishing such an interesting and special book and would like to thank all the writers and artists for their contributions.

Foreword

In our first year of extending the Cadbury's National Exhibition of Children's Art to include a poetry section we were delighted to receive more than 34 000 entries.

The judges had great difficulty, as you can imagine, in deciding which poems out of that number to choose for this volume. Our thanks must go to the judges from the various committees for all their hard work.

Cadbury Limited will be donating the royalties received from this publication to the Save the Children Fund so that the pleasure you derive from this book can be put to the best possible use.

I sincerely hope you will enjoy reading the book as much as I have done and share with me the pleasure of creativity which this publication celebrates.

Adrian Cadbury

Jason Upham

The flowers What grow so high.
My mum do not like The flowers
What grow so high.
My mum cut the flowers
What grow so high.
My dad took the flowers
What grow so high.
Down the tip.

JASON UPHAM
AGE 7

'The Flowers What Grow So High', Jason Upham (7)

Being Me

The Poem

Its hard to get ideas when you're miserable
And tired,
Your mind gets tied in knots which just won't
Come undone.
You've got to write a poem and hope
To get inspired,
You moan and groan for hours and
Still you've not begun.

You chew your pencil down and try to
Make a start,
You kick the sofa twice and feel no better
Then.
So what could be the theme of this
Worthy piece of art,
Spring, the Cuckoo, daffodils, oh dear
Where is my pen.

Daniel Salcedo (11)
(Highly commended)

Me

I worry a lot
Boy do I worry
On Mondays I worry
On Tuesdays I worry
On Every day of the week
I worry
I worry about anything
and everything.

I'd like to be someone
who doesn't worry
Boy do I wish I didn't
worry
Here I go again worrying
about worrying
I wish I didn't worry about
worrying about worrying.

James Cann (11)

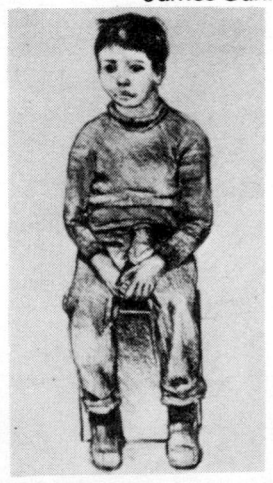

'My Brother Sandy', Iain Sturrock (13)

Mumps

I'm down in the dumps,
Because I've got mumps!
I hope it goes soon—
It's like a balloon!
It hurts when I yawn
And it hurts when I chew,
And sometimes I wish
That they'd change me for new!

Now DON'T call me fussy,
Because I am NOT!
I have to take tablets
And they make me hot!
I can't move around —
(That's unusual for me!)
I can't eat my breakfast,
My dinner . . . OR . . . tea!

I can't go to school
'cos my cheeks are so fat;
I look like a hamster —
I giggle at THAT!
I pull funny faces —
It helps pass the time;
I laid down and thought . . .
Then I made up this rhyme!

Nicola Jane Field (9)

Having a Brace

I sit on the chair, my legs shaking
He takes it out of the impression.
I look at it. Its pink and silver
I feel butterflies in my stomach.

He puts it in my mouth
I can't swallow
Half choking me he takes it out
He looks at it.

I am thinking,
what will people say?
How will I eat?
Will it be strange?
Will I be able to speak?

He puts it back in my mouth
I am beginning to be able to swallow
I learned to take it in and out
Then he says we can go.

Feeling as if I have a sweet in my mouth
I put on a brave face
And go out to meet my problems.

Karen Elkington (9)

Hands

They speak with voices that can't be heard.
They spin, they twist, they bend, they twirl.
They call you from across the street.

They warn you when you make an error.
They stop you when you're close to cars.
They halt, they wave, they say goodbye.

They threaten you with clenched up fists.
They bully the people on the road.
They say 'Be off, and don't come back.'

They comfort you when you hurt your head.
They rub your cheeks when you go to bed.
They say 'There there' when you've had a hard day.

They work all day and never stop.
They wind, they pull, they push, they load.
They tidy, they clean, they do everything.

Robert W. Dunkerley (10)

Toes

Toes are like fishes
Swimming about at the end of your feet;
Never a care in the world,
But to keep hanging on.

Julie Ridd (14)

Blood

I think back, whilst talking to a friend,
My mind's eye roves, turns over
Stones in my memory,
Searching for experiences.

A black, unpleasant, crablike thought
Scuttles out, but is caught,
Held by inquisitiveness,
My brain throbs . . .

Remembering the terrifying pain,
That makes you feel sick,
Thoughts surge, spew forth memories.
Above all, climbs the thought . . .

Of what might have happened . . .
It is best to forget.
The black memory drips rich, red blood.
Life ebbs slowly away.

A bamboo cane, thrust deep in the ground,
Reminds me that once, while riding my bike,
A yellow-brown piece of bamboo
Got rammed up my nose.

I remember little else of what happened then,
Except blood,
Oozing, pouring out of my nose.
And I stood there, helpless.

It is like a tide, going out,
Yet never to return.
Blood gushes forth, unrestrained,
A red carpet to Heaven.

Nigel Timothy Johnson Lake (14)

My Heart

My heart can be a Chinese garden
    Quiet and at peace
But it could be like a Samurai
    All fiery and fierce

My blood may be like a little stream
    Tranquil and at peace
But it can be like a volcano's lava
    All angry and so fierce

Richard Burgess (12)

Freedom in Chains

I have so many ideas.
I want to speak my mind.
I want to be free,
but you won't let me.
My mouth is on a latch,
which you often close.
My mind is a flowing river,
which you try to dam.
I want to fly on the breeze,
but you chain my wings.
I speak my feelings,
you close your eyes to them.
For I am young—
I have no experience,
Or sense.
I am always wrong,
I am your child.

Lesley Curtis (16)

Teenager

I am like a marmalade sandwich—
Half eaten,
Though not completely,
Yet not fresh and new.
Suspended between meringues and biscuits.
Unsure of its next step in life—
Wanting to stay, but bored,
Enzymes reacting, growing mouldy.
I want to be guided—
By the hand – not the mouth.

Melanie Robathan (17)

Fear

Fear makes you feel like a timid mouse.
You're alone in a wood
An owl screeches above you,
You run like the wind.
It's as if you're in a corner by yourself.
You can't close your eyes because you picture bad
    things
In your mind.
At school you're always the odd one out.
You cry when lightning flashes.
You fade away when it thunders.

Gary Godsall (10)

Go Away and Shut Up

I asked my Dad why I had to be quiet
He said
   'Go away and shut up.'
I asked my Mum why I couldn't fly my
Kite she said
   'Go away and shut up.'
I asked my friend why I couldn't
Play with her she said
   'Go away and shut up.'
I knocked on the staffroom door and
Asked for Sir he said
   'Go away and shut up.'
I asked myself why every one was
Saying
   'Go away and shut up.'
But no answer came all I heard
Was
   'GO AWAY AND SHUT UP.'

Colleen Boland (10)

Dreams

I stumbled upon myself
Wandering through oblivion
In the dark, lonely recess
Of my mind.
Entire audience,
Complete cast,
I observed
And was observed
And was alone.

Night in the light
That shines only in darkness
Exhilaration, peace that comes
Only to the unaware.
And tainted only, when
By some trick of that same light
I see its transience
And reluctantly cross my eyelids
Into day.

Alison Hill (16)
(Highly commended)

I Should Like To . . .

I should like to hear the stork flap from place to place
See the bluetit's chirrup, smell the look upon its face.

I should like to taste the moon so big and bright
Touch a ghost a-riding through the still dark night.

I should like to hear the jelly wobble
Taste the turkey cluck, strut and gobble.

I should like to smell the people walk
Catch their words and taste them as they talk.

Robert McKechnie (12)

I Should Like

I should like to touch the scent of a flower,
Wrap it up in a little ball,
Keep it just for me.
I should like to feel the flight of a bird,
The air under its wings,
To hear the dive of its beak
As it soars through the sky.
To hear the sigh of a caterpillar
As it settles down to prepare for a long rest,
To hear its joy for the first time.
I should like to feel the screech of an owl,
Vibration making my fingers tingle with excitement.

Marisa Bailey (10)

The Wild Wave of Happiness

The cold dam of the average
Looms grey and bleak
In the whirling mists
Of my mind's eye.

Over the years
Worry has slowly constructed it.
It grows with each day,
Inexorably bleak, inexorably upward.

Occasionally a wave
Courses through my blood,
A wave of content,
Warming my body.

But, finally, smash,
It destroys itself
Against the icy bleakness
And all is average again.

But a day comes when,
In the middle of an average
Dam-heightening
History lesson,

The headmaster walks in
And the results are announced:
Steve first, Mac second, Nash third,
Andrews fourth

Andrews fourth
The news smacks me.
A surging rumbling frothy whiteness
Races towards the dam.

It crashes into it, victorious,
Annihilating years of work and worry,
Frothing and bubbling it lingers a while
On its triumph.

Then it surges
And with it I race
Wild and mad with joy I run.
Tears fight their way

From my eyes,
Happiness speeds my legs,
I scream and shout,
My face contorted with pleasure.

And now when I recall
That marvellous wild joy
I remember, the higher you build your dam
The bigger the wave that will knock it down.

Dominic Marcel Andrews (14)

Sometimes

Sometimes I lie upon my bed
Sometimes I just lose my head
Sometimes I just think up things
Or pretend I have wings.

Sometimes I think I am flying away
To where it is sunny every day.
Sometimes. Sometimes can you see
I'm very happy being me.

Bethan Jones (7)

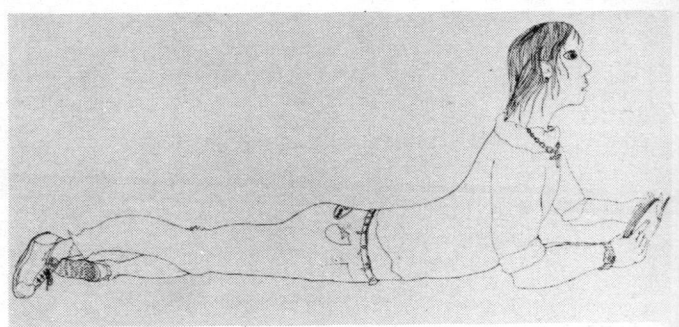

'Self Portrait', James Morgan Williams (11)

Spot On

Imagination.
A fertile valley, nestling in a wilderness,
With a frog hopping about.
A spotted frog.

A spotted frog
Hopping, hoping it won't be seen,
Because a frog should never be seen by a . . .
Lesser spotted frog-eating bird.

I wander around,
Spotting spotted frogs,
And lesser spotted frog-eating-birds,
Spotting spotted frogs.

But lo!
There is the great lesser-spotted, spotted-frog-eating-
Bird,
Spotting spotted frogs as well.

On the horizon I can see a . . .
Small spotted, small little spotted small bird-eating
Frog spotter. Of course, he is spotting frogs.
Alas, alack, they are rare now.

Uncommon are the . . .
Small little spotted small bird-eating frogs.
But, of course, they don't eat . . .
Greater spotted frog-eating birds eating spotted frogs.

Such is imagination.
Incongruous.
Maybe the wilderness isn't so big.

I can see spots . . .

David Russell Watkins (14)

Love

They look,
But neither moves.
A feeling,
Shared,
But as yet unspoken,
Grows.
They smile,
A quiet acceptance.
The beginning.

Kate Challenger (17)

One Day

One day I fell in love.
It was just like a butterfly
Emerging from its chrysalis;
So beautiful, I cried.
It was a bite
Out of an apple,
So sweet its juice
Tasted like honey.
It was a tiny
Baby fist,
Clutching a strand of hair;
A golden thread.
It was a rainbow
Of more than seven colours,
Millions and millions.
One day I fell in love
And I grew wings;
I flew. Briefly

I was a bird,
An eagle, flying
Up and up.
One day, one smile
Meant more to me
Than the whole world.
One day, I sang.
All day, I sang.
But then
My butterfly died
And the apple grew old.
The fist let go of the thread,
The golden hair.
My rainbow
Shattered into
A myriad
Coloured pieces.
My wings
Disappeared,
And I fell
Down and down.
I couldn't
Even
Sing

Then,
One day,

I fell in love.

Rachael Anne-Marie Naylor (14)
(Highly commended)

The Difference is Still the Same

Though it never really got far
What we had was good while it lasted
So much so that if she came back to me now
I wouldn't say no
To being closer than just 'close friends'.

And though it didn't last long
– It should've lasted forever—
If she came back to me now
I'd willingly catch up on love we lost
And patch up the sorrow we both made it cost
Though I'd probably find
That our differences
Are still the same.

Stephen Doolan (17)

'June', Anna Watkins (17)

Other People

My Family

Mummy is nearly thirty,
Daddy's been there before
My brother is four
And I am more
Baby Gemma's just arrived
through the door.

Simon Rainey (7)

My Mum

She teaches children
to play the piano.
Sometimes she burns
the cheese on toast
but only a bit.
Sometimes she tells me off.
When my daddy is cross
I run to my mummy
and hide behind her back.
I act I'm afraid
but I'm not really.

Catherine Milledge (5)

My Dad

My dad is fat
He will soon be thin
Because he is on
A Sponsored Slim
His hair is black
And brown are his eyes
I love him dearly
Because he is wise
I look like him
So they say
I hope I will be
As nice one day.

Lynne Priday (7)

'My Daddy and Me', Helen Louise Bailey (3)

My Dad

My dad could turn water into
Alcohol by breathing on it.
Or strip paint off the walls when
    he spits.

My dad staggers in drunk every night
Kicks the cat at my mum
And gives her a fright.
My dad hates my brother
and he hates him back!
It might be because he has
Set fire to the house
Five times this month.

Denis Byrne (14)

'Grinder at Work', Leon Bickerstaff *(16)*

Mechanics

My father worked above me, a spanner in his hand.
In the lemon sunlight he was a shadow against the
  blue sky;
A delicate blue, almost watery in the heat.
Beyond him yawned a sleepy field of green and
  yellow;
Cowslips nestled in the long grass like drops of
  honey.

But I became oblivious to the call of the summer
  landscape.
The gravel clawed at my bare legs as I sat beneath my
  father,
He dripped oil on my naked hot hands
And ruffled my hair with grimy, thick fingers.

The sun curved down to the hazy horizon
And the odour of searing rubber and sweating grease
Mingled with the soft flowery fragrance of evening.
A breeze delivered each smell to probe my nostrils
And my father rubbed my hands clean with a filthy
  rag.

Diane Susan Burgess (15)
(Highly commended)

Dogs All Over the World

This poem was made up by Sonia as she walked home from nursery school one day, holding the reins of her twin younger brothers who were being 'dogs' for her.

Dogs with their master
Dogs on their own
Big dogs small dogs
Dogs everywhere

Dogs with their leads crossed
Dogs with their own leads
Uptown downtown
Dogs everywhere.

Sonia Watts (4)

I Love Him Sometimes

I love my brother sometimes
But other times I don't
He asks me to do favours
But sometimes I won't.

He is a darling really
But good at fighting me
I just run away and hide
Up the cherry tree.

Kirstie Weir (10)

That's My Gran

Spectacles and hearing aid,
  Weekly pension just been paid.
That's my Gran.

She goes shopping for lots of things,
  Bacon, groceries and tins.
That's my Gran.

Every week she gives us tea,
  Mom, Dad, Rob and me.
That's my Gran.

Curlers underneath her hat,
  Wipes her feet upon the mat.
That's my Gran.

Makes herself a cup of tea,
  Then sits down to watch T.V.
That's my Gran.

I know she loves me, I know she cares,
  Everything she has, she shares.
That's my Gran.

Matthew James Hewitt (11)

Going to Tea with Grandma

I'm going to tea with Grandma
I wonder what there'll be?
A big round cake with a cherry on top,
Some biscuits and a cup of tea.

I'm going to tea with Grandma
She asked me what I'd like.
Jelly perhaps and ice-cream too,
Oh what a lovely sight.

I'm going to tea with Grandma
I'll help her make the tea.
Then we'll sit down and eat it all,
Just Grandma and me.

Alexandra Calvert (7)

Old and Young

She sits all day not moving.
I wonder what's going through her mind
Maybe she's thinking the same as I am
Or maybe she's remembering her childhood.
'You can see what's on the telly if you like'
'Not much,' I said but got up and turned it on.
I looked at my grandma again,
Old and wrinkled, shortsightedly peering at the screen
The programme continued, she fell asleep
Giving the occasional grunt.
I smiled and carried on watching television.
I wonder what she thinks about my generation.

Elizabeth Witt (11)

Visiting Grandad

'Grandad, Grandad!'
'What? Oh it's you is it? Just a mo
Got to undo the chain.
I fought in two world wars you know!'
'Yes I know Grandad.'
'Sit down then.'
'All right, but just for a few minutes
I've got some homework to do.'
'Oh-h that can wait.'
'But . . .'
'No buts, you're as stubborn as your mother!'

Duncan Reid (10)

Old

When the chair is rocking slow,
And the fading eyelids fall,
And the old friends turn and go,
She faces to the wall.
And when people falsely smile
The way they feel they should,
Then leave her to herself,
She feels death is too good.
And as the winter day,
Cold on her lonely view,
Walks its icy way,
She does not remember who;
And faces to the wall.

Alison Jane Carse (17)

'End of the Day', Wayne Catley (14)

Pictures in the Fire

The old man slouches in his tall green armchair,
Staring into the dancing flames of the glowing fire,
His mind wanders, travelling back to the good old
    days.

A plough-man's muscles tense as he trudges behind
    a strong team of gallant shires,
Tugging at the old wooden plough, trying to keep it
    on a steady course.

His patchy shirt dangling from his waist,
He feeds the chattering chickens; scattering seed
    here and there,
Then collecting the freshly laid eggs from the damp
    wooden pens.

Sitting down to a plate of piping hot stovies,
After a long tiring day,
He puts up his feet on the old stool,
Smoking a black pipe and listening to the news on
   the radio.

He stares into the fire with his half-opened eyes,
   then falls asleep,
The fire slowly dies out, just like the memories of the
   old man.

Alexander Paterson (11)

The Major Regrets

Grand, proud, outspoken.
Military, overbearing,
A mouse inside.
He carries terrible secrets,
The regret of marriage into money,
A trapped life.
A lover of war,
His sadist life he would like to relive,
He has killed many,
He needs freedom.
Shut in the cage of pride.
Pills on the shelf have disappeared,
His wife only has a memory.

Edward Douglass Green (11)

The Men on the Bench

Old men on the bench
Sit side by side,
Leaning against each other,
Not saying a word,
Like bricks in a wall,
Silent, still, each dependent on the others.

Now sitting in the sun,
Mumbling something to each other,
Puffing on a cigarette,
Sipping from a bottle,
Their faces a rusty red,
Like the colour of the bricks.

They remember days gone by,
Standing in straight rows with the army,
In rows like the bricks in the wall.
Their strong healthy frames are gone.
Their crooked bones, once straight,
Held them tall and proud.
The bricks never change. Why should they?

Then they begin to crumble,
Bending and shaking,
Disintegrating slowly until the brick wall falls.
Until the fall, they will wait there
Sitting on the bench.

Rebecca Knowland (14)

From Generation Unto Generation

*This was written for an old lady, Mrs Freeman, a friend of mine,
who had lived in Worcester for eighty years. She died on
10th March, 1983.*

You lived in this dirty city all your life,
Never asking for somewhere different, somewhere
    else.
What beauty did you see in this sad city?
Terraced houses crawl beside a stagnant canal,
As the white paint cracks and curls in yesterday's
    town.
What kept you here? Not the glory that has gone,
Saints and kings and battles, the textbook history.
As the brickwork grows a little older, a little dirtier;
I must leave it behind me, I cannot stay.
Yet you stayed here, lived here, died here.
And the city is here, not because of guidebook
    heroes,
Not because of its dingy cathedral, its historic houses.
The city lives because of the small people,
The small people like you, who love, as you loved,
From generation unto generation.

Melissa Emma Barlow (16)

I Know a Face

I know a face, small, white, and round
   of a boy who will never grow up.
He understands little and is not understood.
He is happy and sad, like the people who turn away
Embarrassed by his difference.

I know a face, happy, and surprised
   of a girl who will never walk,
   and worse will never know why.
She lolls in her wheelchair with joyous energy
And sends waves of pity down my back.

I know a face, wrinkled and old
   of a man who will never see.
He stands there staring out across the world
Not daring to cross the road
And when I help him his kind smile makes me cry.

I know faces, some frightening, some happy
Those who will never walk, see, or think.
When I play, they watch, when I learn, they wonder,
And when I grow up, they will stay the same.

Simon O. Abrahams (13)
(Highly commended)

Angel

Angel,
they called you Angel:
rising to a sleazy morning,
with Marigolds in your hair.
Putting on your morning face,
that slight, art-deco smile.
Standing at the window,
the Sun plays lightly with
your mousy curls,
tints a strand with gold.

Taking breakfast,
pale, sweet tea
in a dingy room;
the noises of the Thirties dawn
down past the door.
Three empty bottles on the step,
and a ginger cat,
moth-eaten in the alley, calls.

Angel,
standing on the doorstep,
breathing in the bitter morning.
Hollow, and thin as the April Sun.

> *Sarah Lucy Davies (15)*
> *(Award winner)*

Rasta Man's Colours

Dis is de rhythm of de Natty Dread
de colour of de band 'pon I 'n' I's head
me tell you bout de story of de, Natty Dread
de first colour on de band dat is red

red is de colour of de blood de slave
shed
de Blood of de rasta man, Natty Dread
red is de colour of de blood de slave
shed

Green is de colour of de grass so bright
pon which Ganja grows in de bright sunlight
Green is de colour of de grass so bright
Yellow is de colour of de tropical
sun

'Pon which I'man grows ackey and yam
Black is de colour dis little ballad's 'bout,
'Bout which de rasta man, laugh and
shout

de colour of de man Muhammad Ali
de colour of de King Bob Marley
de great black writer Marcus Garbey
And that is to mention, but t'ree

A' dem is de colour of de Jamaican flag
now dem a' lose their old time slave-
Man's tag.

Robert Kaffash (13)

A Misty Night

London 1880.
A policeman, helmeted and caped,
Pounds his solitary beat.
Through the back streets, and he
disappears into the mist.

He thinks of the warm mug of tea
Waiting for him at the end of his beat,
His torch helps him see through
the mist.
On he walks.

He smells rubbish dumped lazily
in the gutter,
And the wet smell of rain;
The bitter wind clings at his cape,
On he walks.

The houses are dark,
Doors are locked,
Gravel crunches underfoot,
On he walks.

He passes a graveyard,
A mouldy smell goes up his nose,
He gazes at the graves,
On he walks.

Robin Watson (10)

Prisoner

Awakened by the jangle
Of keys in the iron lock
He got up off his rough bed
Feeling strangely numbed.

The long walk down steel corridors
Was cruel and cold
As the echoing cat-walks stretched out
Seemingly endless, fading to blackness.

The gates of 'freedom' opened
And the cold grey light
Smashed against his thin pale face.
Then came the crash as the doors
Clanged shut.

He climbed the stairway
Which would lead him to all wisdom.
If the world was to finish
He would not see the final curtain.

The figure faced the crowd fearlessly,
A sea of empty faces,
The last memory he would have
As the black haze surrounded his eyes.

Memories of his childhood and of his being
Were now a blur
Of colours and sounds. To him
There was no difference between a cold stone floor
And mellow fields.

As colours faded and tones ceased
The sky shattered like thin ice.
He could feel the heat of the
Furnace.

Andrew Challinor (14)

Their Wedding Day

Like snow
Flurries of cold confetti
Fall on the girl
Within a white cage
And freeze the flowers in their prime.
Black, beside her,
Stands the lock to her cage,
So pleased he's the one
To be shutting the door.

Alice Louise Bird (16)

Work and Play

School

Nine o'clock
And it's time for school
Get your satchel,
Get your hat you silly fool,
Pushing and scattering,
Knives and forks clattering,
Sad ones mumbling,
Slow ones grumbling,
Monitors shouting
'Get back and walk.'
Girls crying
Some having a singsong and talk.
Big bullies roaring
Charging
Racing,
Little ones crying
Coming indoors
Putting hats on pegs
Coats being dragged,
Ah! the whistle's gone
Everyone has stopped
Singing a song
School day has begun.
The key turns
The door opens,

Children are in the classroom,
It's quiet now,
People are reading,
People are writing,
People are copying,
Oh ding dong
The bell's gone,
Now it's hometime,
School is quiet once again,
Scrambling and shoving,
Pushing round bends
And corners,
And now they're all home,
School's finished
Until tomorrow.

Julie Nevin (7)

If the Teacher was a Robot

If the teacher was a robot,
Made of Iron and Tin
We could take it all to pieces
And put it in the bin.
We'd loosen all its nuts and bolts
In the metalwork room,
We would weld its mouth tight shut,
And send it to its doom.

Paul Marsh (13)

'Portrait', Hashim David Akib (15)

Day Dreams

Mrs Lifford thinks I'm looking,
But I'm not!
I'm a frog leaping from roof to roof
Crashing each one down.
I'm in a crystal palace with a golden dress.
Mrs Lifford thinks I'm reading,
But I'm a pop singer,
I'm killing a dragon
OH! Gosh, what's she saying. . . .

Isabel Sharman (8)

The Schoolmaster

A daunting Everest of shabby blue books
Looms depressingly before bloodshot eyes.
War-weary, the desiccated man opens the bottom
    book,
As is his time-tested custom.
Deal with the slackers first!
Jones's syntax proves that TV goals rule the Saxons.
Think before you write. Too generalised.

He works contemptuously on the slaughter of his
    subject,
Viciously despatching hurried scrawl,
With gory thrusts and slashes of his dreaded red pen.
Wry comments leak his wish to preserve a battered
    consciousness,
From chalk and talk and the meagre minds of boys.

'Xerox' Smith has fulfilled expectations,
His work bears a ridiculous resemblance to Stein's.
This has been copied! See me tonight.
The gargantuan task is almost finished,
Mediocre marks pigeonholed in the grid of the
    markbook.
He recoils at the prospect of 4C tomorrow,
Hesitates – takes the easy way out, bandas off a test.

Christian Lloyd (15)

Thoughts

All people that on Earth do dwell,
Hope Mr Foster isn't in a bad mood,
Wonder if he's here yet?
Bet he's having his breakfast,
Come ye before him and rejoice.

The piano's wobbly,
Might fall over,
Without our aid he did us make,
Hope Mr Foster's ill,
And for his sheep he doth us take,

O enter then his gates with praise,
Latin room's empty,
Approach with joy his courts unto,
I'm in detention today,
Have to write out 100 lines,
For it is seemly so to do.

Marcus Holburn (10)
(Highly commended)

The Market

I wish I was working
In the market,
People coming and saying
'Can I have this
For my little girl?'
'Can I have that?'
People shouting
'Come and buy,
Only fifty pence.'

Melanie Teasdale (7)
(Highly commended)

Art

The pale-faced poet
With a pained expression
Scrapes out his emotions
And smears them on to the page
Hoping they will sell.

The middle-aged writer
Searches for the right word
And gets up to change the typewriter ribbon.

The scruffy painter
Stares at another faceless nude
Wishing he had enough money
To buy a house in Milton Keynes.

Emma Payne (14)

Aristotle and Ballcocks

They sent me to see the careers man,
He was in a posh office down town,
I tried to be pleasant and friendly,
But all I received was a frown.

'I'm sorry to have to inform you,
But it takes more than three CSEs,
Especially as one is in woodwork,
And the others are only grade threes,

'It takes years of hard work to be one,
Philosophers aren't trained they are born,
And besides your "qualifications",
There isn't a box on the form.'

So he sent me away with a leaflet,
To get on a GYOS*
By the time I walked home from the bus stop,
I thought, 'Oh hell, what a mess!'

When I told my dad, he couldn't stop laughing,
His face went all purple and red,
And when he recovered from choking,
He told me, 'Try plumbing instead,'

So I looked it up on my leaflet,
And filled in the space on the form,
I read up on ballcocks and U-bends,
And reflected the fate of a pawn.

*Government Youth Opportunity Scheme as it was called
when I wrote this.

If Descartes had had this problem,
And Aristotle and Socrates too,
We might not have had great thinkers,
But just think of the showers and loos!

So I went back to see the careers man,
Who said, 'It's a safer idea,
To stick to something more normal,
A job and not a career.'

Valerie Ashe (15)
(Highly commended)

The Dustbin Lorry

There is a hungry monster,
That comes each Wednesday morn,
He sometimes comes before we're up,
Usually after dawn.

He empties all the dustbins,
That people leave about,
He empties them when we're in bed,
And also when we're out.

He eats up all the garbage,
That people put in bags,
Bundles of old newspapers,
And sometimes even rags.

He must get lots of stomach aches,
I'm really very sorry,
That he gets all those aches and pains,
The poor old Dustbin Lorry!

Joanne Jackson (11)

The Turf Cutter

A year ago a green luscious carpet draped
The six-acre field
And in the spring when the cuckoo was first heard
Crystal drops of dew entwined the spider webs
That pieced the sharp grass together
Like a jigsaw.
The field looked flat when a slight breeze
Bent the tips of the timothy grass.
The sheep grazed hard in the field once,
Nibbling until the grass shoots were stubby
And sometimes a pheasant wandered here.

But now on this early spring morning
The turf cutter is awake
Hungrily charging through the field,
Leaving Swiss rolls in neat piles
On top of the wooden stands.
It munches through the field
Leaving hard rooty compact soil
In a maze of fluffy strips of grass.
The hunched, clattery Morris Ford
Looks menacing with the turf cutter strapped
To its side.
The blue paint has rusted, leaving the rough, grey
Surface of a rhino's skin.
He starts another strip.

Thomas Hillier (13)

'Apples and Boxes', Fabia MacDermott (11)

Apple Picking

You're running through the grass
to where it hangs,
Smooth as silk,
a mirror staring at you
Hold it gently like a baby in your arms.

Its home is in a basket now.
Peel it,
inside is its face looking at you.
Taste the freshness melting in your mouth
leave it,
and it stains its colour to brown.
A swollen mushroom lying there.

Rebecca Farthing (11)

53

The Steam Train

The train is leaving London Station,
Heading for its destination.
Clickety, clack. There's no turning back,
The wheels go thundering down the track.
Passengers comfortably settled inside,
Gazing through windows, enjoying the ride.
Passing by villages and small sleepy towns;
A tunnel approaches under the downs.
Out from the darkness into the light,
The end of our journey is almost in sight.

Paula Shorland (11)

Our Caravan

Our caravan is very cosy,
Our caravan is very neat,
Our caravan has a table,
With a big warm seat.

We cook on a gas fire,
We have cheese on toast,
Boiled eggs too,
And sometimes we have roast.

When we are on holiday,
We go to campsites,
We light the small fire,
On freezing cold nights.

We have a hammock,
Instead of a bed,
At night when I'm sleepy,
I lay down my head.

Rona Smith (7)

The Jumble Sale

I like my mummy
She took me to a jumble sale.
She bought me some net to use as a veil,
And she bought me some tap shoes
All lovely and white.
I like to dance in them
From morning to night.

Caroline Elizabeth Moss (6)

Jumble

Tatty jumpers,
Broken toys,
That once belonged to girls and boys
for the Jumble sale.

Broken watches,
Old gas fires,
Electric table lamps with no wires
For the Jumble sale.

Old pots and pans,
Broken tellies,
Unwanted books and smelly wellies
For the Jumble sale.

Kim Forward (11)

Forgotten

I'm forgotten, unloved, and nobody cares,
I'm beside the attic door,
My faded face was rosy once,
But it isn't any more.

I once was a loved and happy doll,
With a pink and smiley face,
With light blue shoes with ribbons on,
And a dress with pockets of lace.

But now my moth-eaten, pale green dress
Is tatty, broken and torn,
And I sit beneath the cobwebs
Miserable and forlorn.

The wood-wormed, creaky floorboards
Beneath me seem to groan,
And I'm sure I'll live here forever,
Sitting here alone.

The only noise I ever hear
Is rats with pattering paws,
And spiders crawl beside me,
And on the attic door.

The strands of yellow wool which were
Once my yellow hair,
Have fallen out, got tangled up,
And scattered here and there.

So I expect I'll stay here now,
Until I'm one day found
For here I lay in tatters,
Bundled on the ground.

Rebecca Hansell (9)

Separation

A pink bunny,
Lies lost
And unwanted.
The teardrops
Of my Mother
Splash sorrow on the ground.
A dog
Lies in front of the fire,
The fire,
Which warmed my heart.
That very fire,
That source of life
Lies cold,
Grey,
Abandoned,
Unattended.
The memories of me,
Lie in a box.
The memories of me
Slip away.

Sally Herod (11)

Blocks

When I build a tower a house or a town
they always say lovely
now please take it down
and put all your blocks very neatly away
I wish for once they
would let them stay

Susan Guest (8)

Fellow Creatures

Spiders

Hanging on a thread, like a wobbly tooth,
Gathering his pipe-cleaner legs to his body,
His pebble-like body shining in the sun,
Creeping like a miniature crab,
Spurts of speed, like blurts of conversation,
Darting to and fro,
Like a yo-yo up and down,
A puppet on a string.

The web glistening like the star of Bethlehem,
A tea-time doily,
A summer bonnet with fly-beads,
Springing trampoline, that can be raked
    down with a hand.
A decorated window,
Magnified, snow-flake falling down,
A fine kind of macrame,
The spider's larder.

Susan Garrett (10)
(Highly commended)

The Beatle

I stared at the beatle I had just squished,
I wished and wished and wished that I had not
squished that beatle,
It looked a beatle of great authority, I
had just squished it and I felt sorry.
Dear Beatle you are in your grave right now,
I hope you do not mind that I told how you got there
but just for you I put a flower in a pot there.

Charley Mallalieu (10)

Mr Honey Bee

From flower to flower,
For more than an hour,
All through my garden,
Never once saying pardon.
He says 'Buzz, buzz,'
On the trip that he loves.
The little bag
Is full of swag.
The little robber
Goes from flower to flower,
Stealing the pollen,
Looking so solemn.
The buzy stranger puts his swag
In his little pollen bag.
Who can this tiny stranger be?
Why! It's Mr Honey Bee.

Rhiannon Lawrence-Francis (7)

A Butterfly

She flutters round the flowers
In the heat of the day
While the excited mosquitoes
Frolic and play
And the crickets chirp
And the pond reeds sway.

She crouches under a leaf
In the chill of the night
While the black bats take
Their meandering flight
And the bad-tempered badgers
Scuffle and fight.

She perches on a flower
When the thrush begins to sing
Misty dewdrops
To tall blades cling
And the butterfly silently
Dries each wing.

Christine McGawley (12)

Fishing

I've fished in the river,
I've fished in the sea,
I've fished before breakfast
and long after tea,
I must say of course that
of fishing I'm fond,
And I caught my best fish
in the old village pond.

Its scales were pure silver,
Its fins were bright gold,
Its tail rainbow coloured,
A joy to behold.
It gazed at me sadly,
Its eyes were jet black,
It looked so unhappy,
I threw it straight back.

Alice Ann Meina (10)

The Fish

Slowly gliding, through a world of twilight,
Swims a fish.
He feels secure, hidden from the world above
Of glaring sunlight, bleak sky.
Down in the river, it is perpetual evening.
Deep in the cool water, he lies,
And with graceful movements, explores
The underwater forest, the waving reeds.
He basks in the quiet blueness,
And when he swims, he makes no noise,
But slips away. His quiet world is bliss,
As he merges with the stream.

Louise Bagshawe (11)

Snakes

The snake glides through the grass.
It is alert, ever watching for prey—
A rustle in the bush,
The angry hiss of a striking snake,
The shrill scream of a dying animal,
As the snake's teeth pump out venom.
A rustle, in the dead leaves
Silently, swiftly, the powerful snake is gone.
    Satisfied,
He glides over the earth,
A ripple of strength,
Ready to kill.
Through the undergrowth,
   Invisible,
   Silent,
Camouflaged by his diamond patterned skin.
He glides on,
Scales rustle and click on the rocks.
Intent on his journey
The snake is stopped by nothing.
He moves gracefully
Sliding along in his silent and colourless world.
Short-sighted and colourblind,
Deaf, no ears
The forked tongue flicks in and out, testing the earth
Smelling.
He glides on, a beautiful line of fierce spiteful power—
Power to kill,
Giver of Death,
Friend of none.
Only his own kind greet him,
With ripples of greeting
He climbs up. Up,
To the welcoming branches of a tree

Looking for eggs.
He is a cold dry predator
Smooth to touch,
His wedge-shaped head
With narrow, evil, black eyes
Never blinking
On and on
Never tired
Creeping.
Stealth is his life.
Never fast. Never slow
On he glides,
Through the grass,
Frightening,
Strong,
Smooth,
Silent,
Unwanted,
Unknown power,
Unloved animal,
Invisible,
Alone.

Jonathan Mayor (11)

A Goldfish

Round the corner, I must go,
Where it leads I do not know,
Round the corner, round the bend,
Will it never, ever end?
I have guessed that it will lead,
To the land of Waterweed,
Or further still towards the sea,
Would be paradise for me.

Lisa Garforth (9)

Goldfish

Jerking across the water
As they pass the side
They get magnified.
Slowly swimming by
Golden fins they have
Eyes that look in wonder.
Glittering as light shines on them.
Floating through the leaves.
Eyes wide like planets
Triangular tail flopping.
Slippery fins
Gliding in the water.
Water swishing in the bowl
Kissing mouth open and closing
Their fins golden.

Karen Jepson (8)

The Hedgehog and the Pincushion

'Good evening,' said the hedgehog, 'would you like
    a drink, my dear?
The wine is quite exquisite in the area around here.
Don't you think the weather's awful for this time of
    year?'
But silence, just silence, was all that he could hear.

'I must say, you look lovely in that wonderful array.
Shall we go and take a walk in the moonlit bay?
Aren't you feeling too well? Would you rather stay
    here?
Barman! Could I order yet another glass of beer?

'Perhaps you'd like to try some caviar?
And then go driving in my car?
Won't you have a drink? Go on, do!'
Never knowing it was a pincushion that he was
    talking to.

Emma Claire Jones (12)

The Death of a Mouse

I climbed onto the buzzard's shadow
And heard the mouse cry from the grass.
Brown claws hooked, turn red.
Screams. . . .
Then the silence crawled back
On shaking legs.

Andrew Wilson (10)
(Highly commended)

The Sunset Squirrel

Autumn copper-gold,
Fox's tail, ridiculously large.
And a small, stiff acorn between neat paws.

A grey squirrel
Behind. I wanted
To cry out, but
Was helpless.
I waited.

Kill!

A strong terror
Red-and-grey whirl,
Biting, taunting murder, over
In seconds.

Weeping into autumn crisp
A rusted pelt
Left behind.
With its lifeless, sunset head
Pillowed
On an acorn.

Sarah-Jane Louise Moll (14)

Old George and the Rabbit

George bagged a rabbit yesterday,
He came home with it dangling lifelessly.

'Didn't think I'd get it,' he said
'I'd just left that trap set
and hidden in that bush,
when along comes a rabbit
all in a rush.'

'He stepped on to the leaves,' said he,
'where I'd left the Ginn,

The brown leaves flew in the air,
That rabbit no longer 'ad a leg.'

At this point in the story,
Old George started laughing . . .

'Did that rabbit struggle
he struggled and choked on blood,
then struggled some more.

He tried to pull the crushed bone away
But I'd set that trap proper.
He choked and his vision swam,
'til his yelps were strangled in
His blood and dying breath.'

That was all yesterday,
Today the Ginn Trap's banned,
I've always wondered why?

Justin Brown (11)

'Sam', Lynsey Foster (6)

My Cat

My cat came home last night,
One battered ear.
It had been in a fight
Only eight lives now.

My cat came home last night
Scratched chin,
Another fight,
Only seven lives now.

My cat came home last night,
Broken tail,
Another fight!
Only six lives now.

My cat came home last night,
Limping as he came.
A fight with a dog.
Five lives left!

My cat came home last night,
With his tail as big as a Christmas tree.
Frightened by a dog.

My cat came home last night!
Wailing as he came.
Sat by the fire,
Ate his dinner.

Later,
Sprinting over the grass.
Jumped over the fence,
Then we did not see him
For a week.

Gone?
Our cat turned up last night,
Hungry and cold.
Ate his food,
Then went to bed.

Now our cat stays,
We think he missed us,
Too much to stay away.

Ben Hebb (11)

Marmalade Sprat

An elegant cat was young Marmalade Sprat,
He sported a top hat and tails,
He wandered along meaowing a song,
And thought about filing his nails.

He went for a walk,
Well more of a stalk,
When the evening air was thinner,
He raised his hat,
At each passing cat,
And pondered on thoughts of his dinner.

He called at the pub,
He was fond of their grub,
His appetite it was stupendous,
He had prawns and chips and savoury dips,
His hunger was neverendous.

Then quite late in life,
He took in a wife,
A beautiful pussy called Flo,
She loved to make wine,
To dance and to dine,
To cook, to knit and to sew.

Then one lazy day,
In a roundabout way,
He noticed his clothes getting small,
The telephone rang and with a great bang,
He exploded all over the hall.

'Cat in a Window', Raymond Lee (17)

Alas and alack what a tragedy that,
The end of poor Marmalade Sprat,
So don't stuff your face, it isn't a race,
Remember the tale of the cat.

Lucy Sheppard (11)

Cats

The cat's eyes glow agate in the firelight
His drowsy paw stretches out to the milk,
Slowly he rises yawning
Laps and finishes.
·

Back again asleep
Gently purring
For endless hours.

Peronel Smith (7)
(Highly commended)

71

Hippopotamus

H orribly fat,
I   ncredible.
P ig-like body—
P ossibly elephant.
O bese it walks
P anting with effort.
O nce in water,
T remendously agile,
A dvances with speed.
M ighty once more.
U nderwater killer.
S ubmarine.

Duncan Bruce (14)

The Robin

Bright, black, dewdrop eyes.
Always alert.
Hopping and jumping,
Twittering and chirping,
Along the ivied wall.
Scarlet satin waistcoat—
Bright against brown,
Delicate legs, ever nimble,
Little head cocked,
To catch every sound.
Then off! A whirr of wings
A flash of red and brown
Gone – but shortly to return.

Anne Grigson (11)

Karen Dawber.

'Birdwatch', Karen Dawber (11)

The Robin

Little bird with red breast,
Sitting in a tree,
Little bird with brown back,
Singing so sweetly,
Lovely brown tail,
And beady black eyes,
Sing near a manger
Where a baby lies.

Amanda Wycherley (7)

'Night Owls', group work, St Wilfred's High School, North Featherstone, West Yorkshire

Owls

Owls are brown and hunt at night,
They go to sleep when it gets light,
They sit in trees watching with sharp eyes,
And they learn to be careful and very wise,
Owls are not often seen by you and I,
But we hear their ghostly hooting across the dark sky.

Katherine Sanders (6)

Spells

In the dark dark wood
Where the old tree stood
There was a silent haunt.
In the hollows of the wood
Owl stood,
With his great big saucer eyes
And his claws and his beak
He catches a mouse
And he swoops over to his old tree house
Where he eats the mouse in great big gulps.
I am glad I was not there
In the dark dark wood at night.

Charlie Forbes (7)

The Swift Owl

The swift owl darting from the skies,
He saw something move, with his big beady eyes,
He landed on a branch watching and waiting,
Ready to dive but not at all hating.

Something moves, the owl is pouncing,
He's struck his prey, now he's climbing,
Sharp claws clutching his precious prey,
Away to eat his kill for the day.

Claire Roman (10)

Sea Swan

Swan flew heavy
over the sea,
clapped white wings in the wind:
snake-neck straight.

Snow swan
settled, pressing on the water;
    watching the faces
of young girls less white than his feathers.
    Grey against grey,
the sea and sky met dull as morning
upon Wales.

Low in the tide,
    two islands
echoed with hollow bird-cries:
January-bare.

Night-dark, in the hills
Fann swims among the reeds;
neck gold-banded.
Present in dreams;
she calls to her mate.

And at Moonset
two swans dawn on the water,
ringed in blue-gold;
part of someone's madness.

Like the swan on our sea,
they unfurl their wings to fly,
    leaving only a ripple on still water.

Sarah Lucy Davies (15)
(Award winner)

The World About Us

Daffodils

A green hosepipe yellow nozzle
Waters winter out of the world
Slowly, slowly it sprays out beauty
Daffodils bring the spring to birth

Philippa North (11)

Spring Flowers

Ladies dancing in the wind,
Wearing their bright yellow bonnets,
Windmill sails behind their heads.

Bells drooping in the hot sun,
Bending over in an arch,
Curving petals all in blue.

Martyn Train (9)

The Daffodil

The daffodil is my lighthouse to spring
It shines a spring message on everything
The leaves and the stem are the stairs and the tower
On top of it all stands this beautiful flower.

The trumpet is the light and the petals are the beams
In the centre of it all the yellow pollen gleams
It shines and shines and shines how wonderful
    it seems
I find it lighting up my dreams.

Sophie Emma McGeorge (7)
(Highly commended)

Sunflower

A sunflower is like
A sun puppet on a stick,
Like a round kite
Floating near the ground
Its tail dangling down,
As if someone had
Tied the sun to the soil
So he could see it
Day and night.

Samantha Waters (12)
(Highly commended)

'Buttercups', Nigel Owen (15)

New Trees

On the stretch of waste ground over the back
They have planted new trees. Over four miles
Of grassy dips and levels, fifty
To a hundred young saplings scatter: thin
And spindly, swaying in the softest breeze.
    Each alone, they spike the sky-backed rises
    And dot the hollowed levels; each separate
    And frail, they quiver under frozen skies
    While crows, beating like falling water, rise.
The trees remain: frozen in brittle air.

In the short eyeblink of a hundred years
They will still be there, though I will be gone.
By then, the dark earth will be laced with roots
And the sky embroidered with branching twigs:
Day on day will root them more firmly
In local soil, making them a landmark;
And thicker, more straight, they will moan at night,
Become a part of the expected sounds.
    They will become splinters of endurance:
    Remaining, though things around will change;
But by then, I will be dead in earth.

Mark Berry (17)
(Award winner)

'Beech Wood', Victor Lewis (14)

The Pinetree

The wind baffled the pine making it moan
and screech, to scare the brave child's heart;
to wing, to whine across the hill, the hill on which
a cluster of nine pines doth stand like bony trolls
staring all o'er the land.

The wind ravaged the pine, standing like
a crippled man looking over the grey sea in all
weathers.

What a life, a life of melancholy, loneliness
to moan of the times by gone; to sing with music
far beyond our human reach, music that no hand
could pluck or bow, music sweet, music wasted
o'er the cold bleak sea.

Nicholas Korth (11)
(Highly commended)

The Fallen Tree

Cracked by the wind
Massive smooth splinters
Maze for an ant
Fresh white against dirty bark
Scattered branches
Defenceless
Railings squashed into a cradle
No use but firewood
Leafless for ever
Reason for willow to weep
Home of birds and woodworm
Unarmed enemy of the wind
More than a scar to show.

Richard Philip Burgess (9)

The Willow Tree

Over the stream the willow bends
Swinging her drooping limbs.
Some of her longer swaying arms
Reach down to where the trout swims.

Even the gentlest of breeze
Can move her hanging twigs,
But the more fierce wind can
Make them dance in jig!

Victoria Collins (11)

At Trentishoe

Above the cove,
The shepherd strings his sheep,
Tracing stone circles in jade grass.

In the heavy sky,
A buzzard steals the wind's mouth,
To swallow the voice of the herd.

Sarah Knibbs (15)

Building Site

From granite rock to shattered brick
Great jaws devour; the hinges thick
With clinging mud, and groaning loud
They stoop for more; the steel neck bowed
In sharp descent. From teeth to gut
The cables stretch with piston, nut
Controlled by one – one man alone
Has power to chew up earth and stone.

With levers at his hands he has
The strength of twenty men and as
The iron head tears up the ground,
It piles the innards in a mound.
The gaping wound begins to seep
With muddy blood. 'Tis now we weep
For once this graveyard, rubble-strewn
Was peaceful field; now ripped and hewn.

Emma-Louise Jones (16)

The Old Factory

A disused track,
Leads up to the old factory,
The grass muffles my footsteps.
As I enter the desolate building.
Bang! Bang! my footsteps echo,
On the hard floor,
The quietness hits
Like a cold wind.
A chill moves through my body,
As though I was invisible,
My presence moves the dust,
Everything watching,
Checking my every movement,
The walls full of strength,
Bend under the weight of time,
An old glove lies in one corner,
Discarded by a forgetful worker,
A reminder of long ago.

Men joking,
Throb of machinery,
People engrossed in their work,
Treating the machines like old friends,
A bell clangs – time for a break,
The smells of food,
Turn into a musty odour of damp,
Voices calling, calling.
Die into the solitude of it all.

Like a smack on its face,
The workshop is closed down,
The employees, its only friends,
Are told to leave,
Discarded, rejected,

Like old rusty tools,
Clink, clank the machines stop dead,
The monotonous hum has gone,
Disappeared into the sounds of years long past,
Like an old man,
They lose all recognition of time.

My imagination takes over,
I feel frightened and uneasy,
I leave the building,
Sadness piercing my heart,
The factory is helpless,
I could never bring back the past,
I run, run, run,
Never to return.

Louise McSorley (11)

Underground

It is dark and gloomy underground,
not a whisper not a sound,
but a tap of a badger,
sipping sap of roots of a sycamore tree.
Tangled roots you can see,
grey with mould,
wet and cold,
a soily mass,
with worms and grass.
No birds to see.
No world to see,
but a dark gloomy den,
unseen by men.

Suzanne Cottam (11)

High Force – a Northern Waterfall

High Force looked white and fresh
Like a ghost
In a long splashy dress
Like a pretty princess.
It was taller than a telephone post.
In 300 miles I liked it most.
Puddles and streams I like them all
But very best – that waterfall.

Kevin McAuslan-Crine (7)

Silent Woods

In the midst of a black wood
A moonlit cottage stand silhouetted against
    the darkness.
No light flows through the curtained windows
Except a glow from the dying embers.
It trickles through the ebony frames.
The dog sleeps in his snug cushioned basket
While the cat slinks noiselessly about the
    undergrowth,
Gliding round corners, his eyes sharp as needles,
Searching for his prey.
A spiny hedgehog scurries timidly to the doorstep
Where a saucer of milk waits for him.

'Snow Scene', Vicky Lunney (14)

Shy badgers are feeding and the tracks of a fox
Follow on to a lair.
Father fox is scavenging for a shrew.
Daytime animals slumber dreamily.
'Tu-whit to-whoo' is the recurring cry of the
    hunting owl.
Mice scurry everywhere to escape this
    scavenger's talons.
The pearly glow from the moon throws shadows
    on everything.
Diamond stars twinkle.
Everything is quiet.

Annabel Neal (11)

My Country Rides

This is where you'll find me,
Galloping on my horse,
In the valley, in the field,
In the field of gorse.

Where the streams go hurrying,
Where the mountains end,
This is where I am found,
On my four-footed friend.

Where the forest's thick with trees,
Where the birds sing on the breeze,
How black my horse how blue the sky,
How green the trees while the wind whistles by.

Where a field of barley lies,
Where poppies grow on every side,
Where rabbits play most of the day,
That's where we often ride.

Where a cliff juts into the sea ,
Where the sand is just for me,
We canter and canter for hours alone,
Past the sunset we'll travel home.

Jeannie Strong (7)

The Scarecrow

Life?
Not quite.
Just a dull sensation,
Of long brown fields,
And of long dark nights.

How long have you been here?
Who is to say?
A month? A year? A day?
Here I was placed,
And here I will stay.

Why don't you run away?
What with?
With rime-ridden legs?
Or with soggy straw masses?
No, here I will stay!

What is your job; what do you do?
I don't know, I'm really not sure.
I think it's to stand here, to stand here all day,
And watch the birds eat the corn,
And laze the day away.

Richard Morgan (14)

'The North-east Coast', John Close (17)

A Sea View

Salty rough waves curl on to the beach and foam
    sprays on to the seaweed covered green rocks.
Crabs skittering across the sands, scurrying under
    rocks to hide.
Wind howls through the remains of an old
    fishing boat moored on the sea wall.
Jagged rocks stick up out of the water.
Seagulls call while flying round and round
    above, waiting for a catch.

Susannah Commings (8)

The Sea

The sea is a hungry dog
Begging for food to swallow up.
It leaps,
It bounds
Through the air
Like a playful pet.
It's ready to catch its victim.
Readily eating everything,
A shoe perhaps,
Or a ring.
The sea will eat anything.
The sea is a hungry dog.

Susan Mantle (11)

A Sea Pool

A sharp, quick, streak, darts across the rock,
Covered in a shade of delicate brown.
The rainbow shades of a shell,
Catch the rays of the sun
And spread glows over the sand,
Leaving a miraculous display of sparks.
Mother of Pearl glistens lovingly, over the antics
of her children.
As does the crab,
Alive and alert under a weed.
The liveliness of the inhabitants
Who go about their business,
Makes the mortal
Wonder. . . .

Varry McMenemy (11)

Still and Yet . . .

Motionless and tranquil lies the tropical forest.
Still yet not still.
As the flora can be felt grasping for air
Lianas choke and smother,
Aerial roots hang limp with moisture.
Green light, green sound, green leaves, green green,
Fighting for light in the green kingdom.
Silence is broken by a single piercing screech,
A howler monkey swings from a branch.
This is the signal for fauna to take over flora
Every leaf rustles as the animals awake
Howling, growling, grunting,
Lumbering, grumbling, tumbling.
Rainbow-coloured macaws glide from tree to tree,
Humming birds hover from flower to flower,
Slippery snakes slither from root to root,
Caymans float from lily to lily,
Monkeys swinging from branch to branch,
Jaguars stalking with cunning
Sleepy alligators sunning,
Rushing and pouncing,
Noisy and clawing,
Noisy is the forest
And yet quiet.

Natasha Bickman (13)

The Raindrop

Tiny, almost spherical
mound of shimmering
light
suspended in suspense
from crinkled
hand of green

Drip
falling through space
and time
with smoothness of speed
a spiral tube
through specks of air
leaving velvet void
and yet to where

Splat
frozen claws
punch out life
sudden cruel
drastic death
sends pinhead spray
a trillion fairy lanterns
lights twinkled and
went out.

Sheila Symon (17)

The Rain

I opened my eyes
And looked up at the rain,
It dripped in my head
And flowed to my brain.
So pardon this crazy thing I just said,
I'm just not the same since there's rain in my head!
I walk very softly,
I step very slow
I daren't do a handstand
'Cos I might overflow!
All I hear as I lie in my bed
Is the shlishity-shloshity of the rain in my head!

Jenny Young (11)

Raindrops

A breath of wind
And raindrops
Come splintering noiselessly
Down.

Images of crystal
Silently detonating.

A great thing is made humble
In a drop of silver.

George Brendon (10)

'School in Winter', Simon Derek Hartley (12)

La Pluie

'Let the rain fall!'
Cried the weather god.
And lo, in full resplendent force,
The rain fell!
Sleek and shimmering grey
Spangling its forceful, straight-laced path
Downwards.
And below,
The animals—
Softly scented of stale and dampened furs,
Pelted, small and frightened,
Squirrels, rabbits, foxes, weasels,
All the insect world fluttered and floated,
Struggling to stay airborne
'Neath the bullets, silvery sent from heaven.
Trees bowed respectfully,
Leaves and membrane greenery
Donned ballroom diamante,
Waltzed breezily with the musty wind
In time with the xylophone clarity
Of raindrop bells.
Flowers, rainbow hued, were freshly frosted,
Fingers of rain extended,
Graciously caressing and painting every
Little corner of nature's design,
Translucent iridescent, wetly melting
Silver.
And the rains ceased.
'I am pleased with my handiwork!'
Called the god,
And he framed his masterpiece
– A rainbow.

Brynn Leadbitter Younger (15)

Icicles

Sparkling crystal
clutching
the eaves

a tapering
spiral
glistening in
the winter
sun
melting
slowly
slowly
clinging to
the last
dying

drip
drip
drip

Angela Wozencroft (13)

Ice

Cold, sharp, splintering, brittle,
Like crushed, crystallised sugar,
Cold fingers grip round leaves,
Fossilising and glazing;
The sun unfurls its tight grip
and fades
The bright white—
To nothing.

Alison Ross (12)

The Wind

Quiet is the wind,
Still as can be,
Only the birds singing,
Can be heard in the trees.

Strong is the wind,
It opens my door,
Sends my newspaper
Across the floor.

Mighty is the wind,
On a stormy day,
Rain lashes against me,
And I cannot play.

Paul Beet (7)

The Wind

The wind blows things over
and hurries away.
It picks houses up and
makes them sway.

The trees think that
wind is their king.
They bow down their heads.
The wind makes them swing.

Christian Lloyd (7)

The Wind

Wind whips and lashes at my hair,
Litter looks like butterflies.
I play 'Astro Wars' with leaves,
Dodging them and shooting them down.
Litter makes a good playmate for running with.
Scurrying clouds make moving pictures,
Hiding the sunrise.
Windy days make me feel excited.

Mark Anderton (11)

Spring

The sheep and cows are eating,
My mam is spring cleaning,
The snow has retreated
Back to the mountains,
The paper boy is shouting
'Read all about it'
The postman is posting,
The weather is hot
It is spring.

George Sheppard (7)

'Kingstown Meadows – Carlisle', David Frith (14)

Childhood Summers

The sun, a hot pearl,
Seered behind a heavy
Canvas of cloud.
Below, pansies cowered
In the crusty earth,
Begging liquid affection,
As the thick, sweet air
Floated by;
Teasing lines of damp linen,
And breathing on regimental gardens;
Battlefields of lawn
And parades of hollyhocks.
We, rebellious of the heat,
Squashed orange berries
And played with tiny dolls
In miniature jungles.
Darts of rain struck suddenly;
We squealed and fled under

Its vehemence.
Clattering down the slate passage,
I fell;
Grey grazed knees, shaking sobs,
Soothed by Mother's healing kiss
And the promise of rhubarb and sugar.
Hot wet afternoons.
Surrendered to warm, slow
Evenings.
Distant church bells
Made their ancient plea
And lawnmowers grated and hummed
While the chuckle of sparrows
And starlings,
Jiggled the sherbet air.
Summer sounds faded,
As I lay cocooned
In a golden room,
The pink fairies of sleep
Climbing through my window.
Then, dreams were made of
White horses, dandelion clocks,
And glittering wisps
Of future Christmases.
Now, they are of
empty houses, silent streets
and strange whisperings
That unborn children
Will never enjoy
The sensuous feasts of summer,
Nor ride white horses
Through meadows and meadows
Of smiling dandelion clocks.

Sarah Jane Quellin (17)
(Highly commended)

Poem

Bottled plums
Ripened
By the summer sun.
Ooze
With sticky juice,
A wasps' paradise!
Bramleys
As big as
Your hand
Enough
To make an
Apple pie
The leaves
Of the fruit trees
Flutter to the ground,
Bronzed and yellow
These colours
Cannot be made
In pictures or
Patterns
Only
Sir Autumn
Can make
Russet red,
Pale yellow and the
Red streaks of
An apple.
I smell
Autumn
Every place
I
Look.
The dying leaves
or the
Scents of
Apples
and
Bonfires.

Joanne Oliver (11)

Autumn Leaves

when autumn comes leaves go golden brown.
they fall like falling feathers
they turn like tumbling waves.
that's what autumn's like.

when autumn comes leaves go golden brown,
when you walk on the fallen leaves they
crackle like your cereals in the mornings.
they look like chipped wood,
that's what autumn's like.

when autumn comes leaves go golden brown,
they hang like bats fast asleep and
when the wind blows they sway
side to side, front to back,
that's what autumn's like.

when autumn comes leaves go golden brown,
sometimes they fall in pairs like birds flying,
sometimes they fall in big bunches
with nuts on top and
that's very nice.
that's what autumn's like. . . .

Victoria Lyons (8)
(Highly commended)

October

I give you nuts in cloaks of green
I give you berries black and red
Conkers, polished bright and clean
Dropping down from overhead.
In the fields for you I grow
Mushrooms at the dawn of day
And on the hedges high and low
Old mans beard, soft and grey.
I give you leaves of red and gold
I bid the ivy spread its honey,
And though my nights are long and cold
My autumn days are sweet and sunny.

Timothy David Neale (8)

Winter

Cold and dark,
The wind is whistling,
Only the chimney smoke is moving,
Blown by the breeze,
Round and up in skipping circles.

A choir sings in the ancient church,
With red noses and chapped lips,
They try with poor result,
To keep up the Christmas cheer,
To them winter means carols and sore throats.

As the dark curtain descends over the town,
Windows are brightened with
Christmas lights and radiant candles,
Sparkling like stars in the night.
To the inhabitants,
Winter means electricity bills and presents.

A small sparrow puffs out his feathers,
And braces himself against the wind,
To him winter is just,
A test for survival,
And he dreams of his friends far away.

A tramp spreads out his newspaper,
On his park bench bed,
He lies down with stiff limbs and a cold heart,
To him winter means begging and others' goodwill.

Cold and dark,
The wind is whistling,
Only the chimney smoke is moving,
Blown by the breeze,
Round and up in skipping circles,
Winter means nothing to it.

Eleanor Phillips (13)

Winter

Wind-withered grasses by an ice-smoothed stream
Where grey mist hangs like the cold breath of winter.
Bare, brittle branches where no birds sing,
Stilled their voices in this cold, hard land.

Laced with white, the world lies sleeping
Through days that hardly heed dawn's calling;
Short hours of grey light and long hours of darkness
In an ice-bound world where nothing stirs.

Snow that falls softly, deep-thatching our roofs;
Snow that comes creeping, stealthily stealing
Up frost-feathered window panes,
Dreamily drifting and shrouding the land.

Frost-silvered trees, traced in the sky;
Harsh stinging sleet, hard-driven by wind.
Beautiful winter and merciless winter,
Eventually losing to your enemy, Spring.

Joanne Crittell (13)

Legend and the Supernatural

The Dragon

Brazen jaws,
Red with flame.
Crocodile teeth.
Leaping and pouncing.
Firework nostrils,
Roaring and screaming.
Banging and crashing.
Hungry, looking for food.
Fiery eyes,
Flying angrily in the night.
Glittering scales.
Frightening claws.
Silver wings,
Terrifying jaws.
Glittering scales in the night.
Shining eyes, gleaming bright.

Michelle Kee (7)

The Year of Ghosts

In January ghosts rapped on the doors,
In February they howled up on the moors.
In March they were helpful pulling up weeds,
In April, all four weeks they did such dreadful deeds.
In May they threw all our money away,
In June they hid our toys when we were going to play.
In July they played such dreadful tunes,
In August they lost our swimming costumes.
In September they ate our apples, rosy and red,
In October they stripped our bedclothes right off
    our beds.
In November they took our breath away,
In December they all went away upon
    Christmas Day.

Catherine Brereton (7)

The Midnight Ghost

The night is grey,
The sky is dark,
The owl hoots on the post.
Mounted on a spirit-steed,
There rides the midnight ghost.
Upon the dark horizon,
A shape is clear to spy,
As the midnight rider travels,
Ghostly black against the sky.
With a cloak around his shoulders,
Round his steed a ghostly glow,
Every night at stroke of midnight,
I survey the rider go.

They say it's all a story,
That it never has been seen,
But there's always ghostly hoof-marks,
Where the midnight rider's been.

Victoria Osborne (10)

The Spell of a Witch

I am making a magic spell,
With a toad and a goblin's yell
A phantom's scream, a dragon's feather,
It smells as good as good as ever.
With frog's toes and lizard's legs,
I think I'll add some rotten eggs.
I scream and shout I moan and yell,
I've just found a snail's shell.
I'll add a pinch of dirty weather,
With a poison dragon's feather.
I stir my brew, I stir my brew,
Some for me and some for you.
Spooky, spooky dark and damp,
I met a wizard I met a tramp.
The wizard gave me a puppy dog's tail,
The tramp gave me a toad and a snail.
I stir my brew, I stir my brew,
Some for me and some for you.
I'll add some poison I'll add some blood,
I think it smells rather good.

Gillian Parker (9)

Continuation of Robert Burns' 'Tam O' Shanter'

. . .When he got hame an in the door
    She bellowed oot a frighfu' roar
    'Where ye been hauf the night
    An why are ye lookin' awfy white?'
    'A've seen witches, warlocks and Auld Nick!'
    'Ach' she said 'Yoo an' yur lies
    Ya mak' me sick!'
    Wi' her naggin' wha wid think
    Seein' witches wisna drink
    'That'll be the last nicht ah go oot boozin'
    Ah'll sty in ma big bed snoozin'.
    That wis the last time he went oot at nicht
    Efter seein' that terrible sicht.

George Graham (11)

The Seafarers

Seafarers trading
Viking longship
Vikings ready to plunder
I am Odin.
God of Warriors
Wondrous in the eyes of men
Those warriors who die
In combat
Shall come to me
In Valhalla
But those who die
In their homes

Of sickness
Shall go to Hell.
I am Thor
God of Thunder
My hammer blows echo
In earthquakes
Of destruction
My eyes of lightning
Pierce the hearts of traitors,
Nothing can withstand Mjolnir,
Thor's mighty hammer
Thor shall not rest until every foe is dead.
The Northmen are traders,
Bringing animals' skins.
They decorate themselves
With golden armbands.
They are never seen without their weapons.
They are men of great courage.
There will come an age of death,
Brothers will kill each other.
Odin shall go to fight Fenrir.
Fenrir will devour Odin.
Then Odin's son will kill Fenrir.
Thor shall go to fight the sea serpent.
But he shall be killed
By the serpent poison.
Old warriors die
Kinsmen die
There is only one thing that never dies
The fame of a brave man.

Imogen Hemy (10)

The Sun Rose High

The sun rose high in the heavens.

Icarus bound on his freedom flight,
His spirits high
But his vision blinded by the sun's cruel rays,
That ruthlessly attacked his waxen wings.
Earthward he fell.

And the sun shone high.

Ploughman carves his endless furrow
Deep in thought.
No time to glance at the falling child.
The day is short – his horse plods on,
Toil and toil.

As the sun reigns high.

Shepherd guards his bleating flock,
In tender care.
No time to pray for the plunging boy,
Look after the sheep, rescue the lamb,
Watch and watch.

And the hot sun glowed.

Fisherman cast your rod to the sea,
The baited hook.
Curse the boy, for scream and splash.
Wind in the line, count the catch
In scales and blood.

The sun sank low.

Captain stay your valued course,
Your sails full.
Your pity show for the drowning child;
But waves envelop, tides make clean,
Journey on.

The sun hides now in the heavens.

Jane Clark (14)

Eloïse

Lonely he walked,
And his feet sounded on the
Dark pavements of his memory;
And the lights of the street
Danced in his tears.

Lonely he cried,
And tears washed his mind
Free from the agony of love;
And his heart sang the song of sadness,
With his tired soul.

Lonely he fought,
With the emptiness of his life, and
The reflection of his thought;
As the mirror shattered and
The pieces fell distorted.

And alone he walked, wept and fought.

Alexandra Helen Zoë Crompton (13)
(Highly commended)

Space Derelict

Hanging in the inky blackness of space unknown,
A monument to the long forgotten race eons past.
Alien.
A mangled hulk of iron made by inhuman hands.

Blackened by blinding jets of flame,
Forged into a shapeless mass by fires from hell.
Empty.
A wreck caused by countless battles, and devoid
    of life.

Inside the empty shell deformed by time
All is dark; smothering dust hangs in the empty void,
Suspended.
Dirt trapped in each hidden cranny. Unclean.

Completely deserted of life, human or otherwise,
Only the cold vastness of space, the infinite vacuum.
Forgotten.
Viewed only by the far distant stars: a derelict.

Steven Ashford (11)

Life and Death

Prayer Before Birth

Let me, the womb dweller, live to see birth.

May my cell of sustenance deliver me unscathed
Into the breathless, rushing trauma of life.
May I not starve in the ghettos of humanity;
Nor live bloated on the fat of the poor.

As I am so safely suspended here,
May I be in the life after life.
May my time on earth be peaceful;
Not harassed by the tormented fantasies of idiots
    and fools.

Let me pass into old age with dignity.
May I not be impaired in vision or sense
Or troubled by collapse of health, so that
I may pass out of this life as I came in:
                    With Hope.

Jacquelyn Louise Barker (14)
(Highly commended)

Programmed Life

(based on a BASIC computer progam)

INPUT one new human being, a soft pink sponge
    to soak up a world's emotions.
LET it grow and develop free from the womb, free
    to ask and be told.
READ into that child's mind all society desires
    him to know—
DATA of arithmetic, obscure poets, and how life
    should be lived.
FOR boy TO man STEP ten years on, older, wiser,
    a perfect pupil of his mistakes.
IF that man is successful THEN give him a car,
    a suburban semi, and a wife that doesn't
    always nag.
IF he has failed THEN cast him out, a reject of
    the society which sets the rules.
GO TO that man in his last hours, whatever he was
PRINT out a life that has failed, before men or
    before God.
    It waits only for the last line.
END

Suzanne Furber (16)

Daily Life

At morning, we know
Life is confused impressions,
Tangles of senses. . . .

By afternoon, we
Know life is slow dragging down:
Such burden bends us. . . .

On the edge of sleep,
We know that death will be like
Eternal falling. . . .

Mark Berry (17)
(Award winner)

To My Late Father

Like an infantile fantasy,
You are always here—
But the child's imaginary companion
Is a friend,
To occupy his hours.
Your presence haunts me,
But I cannot make you go.
I have the power to banish you—
But I dare not use it,
For you are now so much part of me,
That, without you,
I may be nothing.

Jane Light (14)

'Ram's Head', Louise Rosbotham (15)

The Skull

The ancient head
Stood solidly,
Anchored in the ground.
Held there by stones,
Wood, and soil,
Aged, bony,
And very tough.
Moss held in every crack and cranny,
Snails investigating every hole,
Looking, peeping,
Then going in.
Woodlice shared
This grubby skull,
With spiders, snails,
And the occasional worm.

Claire Dunster (11)

Skeleton

Smooth and white,
Gleaming bright,
The skeleton lies in an ancient coffin,
Once a mass of rotting flesh,
Now a shining network of bones.

James West (11)

Mayday at Blackpool

As the first rays of summer sun descend from the sky,
The tourist swarm arrives, ice-cream tongues, hats,
Bouncy beachballs, ballooning faces;
Fat, white marble-column legs and hair
Drawn unwillingly from their faces
To catch the golden rays of sunlight.

Pictures in the sand, assorted dots on a blue
    sheet of sky and sea,
Sandy lolly hands, wind and sea-blown hair.
Dancing dogs, biting, playing with beachballs,
Kicking sand at unsuspecting victims.

Surfers, riding the waves, screams, and squeals
Of delight as little children smother in the frothy
    water;
Figures hurdling the sea, boys having a 'dare',
Throwing themselves into the oncoming traffic of
    pounding waves,
Until one wave cannot stop in time—
The boy is gone!

One scream, but no attention
Another, and soon, a few people force their
 heads from the newspapers;
The chatter stops. The scream casts a spell
Over the sunbathers. Their minds go numb.
Their bodies turn to stone.

Soon, a brave body breaks the spell—
The 'dare' boy is brought in.

Other people come out of the spell, and
Crowd like ants fighting for food, around the boy.

Many gasp in fear as they realise that only the
 body is there.
The mind and soul are now dancing with the waves—
Part of the sea's many secrets.

Wendy Moore (13)

Murder on the Chessboard

The chessboard stood in the darkness of the night,
All the squares lit up with a brilliant light
There stood the chessmen red and white,
Stealthy and silent in the darkness of the night.

A man drew near, a few lights dimmed
He was very neat, and his hair was trimmed.
He wore a bishop's mitre, and a robe of white;
Silently he crept along in the darkness of the night.

Another man came, he looked like a king,
Dressed in red, with a diamond ring.
He went and stood on a square that was white;
And waited there patiently in the darkness of the
    night.

The bishop crept up, following his band,
And slowly, but silently, raised his hand,
As the dagger came down, there was a flash of white,
And all was silent, in the darkness of the night.

The grisly deed done, the bishop went;
(There is a suspicion that he was sent)
But behind him, the chessboard, giant and
    gleaming white,
Kept its long, lonely vigil in the darkness of the night.

Christian D. Hayter (10)
(Highly commended)

The Fist Descended

the fist
descended
the sickening crunch
the snapping limb
the stifled scream
that tears the heartstrings

(but no one moves)
the shout of anger
the dripping tear
(but no one moves)
the pleading,
the hate,
(but no one moves)
not my business
nothing to do with me

(still no one moves)
until
the misplaced
blow
the final destruction.
neighbours appear
the child, a
shrunken corpse
in death
lies prone
horrified
indignant;

appalled
neighbours

'Imaginary Landscape',
Jacquelyn Trew (14)

phone
the police

contented
the neighbours
disperse
'i've done my duty'

but what about
the child
dear contented
neighbours
it's dead dear
neighbours;

and you were too late
dear neighbours

again.

Guy Soar (16)
(Highly commended)

This Day and Age

This Day and Age

The West demands an up in wage,
The Third World lives to grovel.
The West resides in the modern home,
The Third World in a hovel.

The West decides to ban the bomb,
But puts it off 'til later.
The Third World starts another coup,
Against a crazed dictator.

The West is building satellites,
To benefit mankind.
The Third World strives to live each day,
On food it cannot find.

The West prepares its future,
It'll always find a way.
The Third World sits alone and prays,
To live another day.

'Here and Now', Bridget Smith (17)

And when the West sees the certain death,
The Third World has to greet.
It shouts that something must be done
BUT NE'ER THE TWAIN SHALL MEET.

Craig Skelton (16)

Christmas Thoughts

Oh to be in India, now that winter's come,
Sweltering heat and lack of food,
But nothing can be done.

Oh to be in Africa, now that Christmas rings,
Poverty and homemade shacks.
How sweet the choir boy sings.

Oh to be in Poland, now for festive cheer,
Internment camps and martial law.
We'll go another year.

Oh to be in Belfast, now the snow has come,
Fights, explosions, massacres.
It doesn't sound much fun.

Oh to be in England, now that robins call,
Tinsel, baubles, shiny stars
The hypocrisy of it all.

Chloë Thomas (14)
(Highly commended)

The Computer, Man's Creation

>The computer returns my stare
Impassively. A slight hum
Emits from I know not where
And its answer to my sum
'Silly.' But it does not know
How it implicates itself
Its mind swift as a doe

And nimble as an elf
But yet more stupid still
Than the tiniest little beast
That quietly drinks its fill
Of Nature's statistical feast.

>It cannot hear, though it could talk
If I bought it a voice-synth. And
It cannot see, it cannot walk
Though it could feel with a robot hand.
I am its input from the world,
I am this computer's best friend.
Though for hours I sit curled
Before it, thinking, I still tend
To philosophise more than I process
Because, together we make a team
TERRAC never needs to guess
And hardly interrupts its dream

>Of sheep at 2MHz.
And though my thoughts are far more subtle
It knows the ionic valency of lead
(Which is 2). Its registers shuttle
Through Kilobytes of memory, and so when
The answer's found, the printer clatters
Obedient to *its* master. The computer then
Is aware of the datum that matters
And shows it to me. But only I,
Though on the keyboard I may hammer,
It is only I who really know why
It is computer and I the programmer.

Jonathan Harley (15)
(Highly commended)

Can Johnny Come Out to Play?

Do you remember, Johnny,
When we were kids?
How we used to play soldiers
Just for kicks?
Do you remember, Johnny,
When we stormed the traffic island.
Now we're storming the terrorists
In Northern Ireland.

Do you remember, Johnny,
When we played with toy guns?
How we used to say
That we wished they were real ones?
Do you remember, Johnny,
Pretending to die with great zeal,
The kids in Crossmaglen
Are doing it for real.

No need no more
To go making toy guns,
After all, haven't you
Seen all the little ones
Calling at their friends' homes
With their petrol bombs?

Johnny,
What the hell went wrong?

Do you remember, Johnny?
We used to marvel at the Cortina man,
The kids in this city
Are more used to climbing into Chieftains,
Do you remember, Johnny,
Climbing on the van for something to eat?
The last one to do that here
Ended up with no feet.

No need no more
For the leaders to say,
'A solution must be found',
There is no way
To combat the fear
That we've found here.

Johnny,
What the hell went wrong?

Johnny,
Where have you gone?

Johnny,
When are we going home?

I think I hear my mother
Calling me
Home for tea.

Kevin Ward (16)
(Highly commended)

A Black Shadow

A black shadow flew across the sight before him.
It was a crow,
And it passed over the scene of the setting sun in the
 pale opal sky
And the sinking mist that lined the valley's length.
Furthermore the picture was clouded by his breath as
 it rose in clouds
Like steam clouds, flowing from the Berlin train.
Along the wooded valley side a man ran and shouted
 loud,
'Sehen sie! Gefangene!'
Through the icy dusk three figures ran, grey-clad
 with rifles—
Pointers to the sun about to touch the ground.
Above the trees the echo rose until it hit the sky
And then, it settled down once more to fall within the
 stranger's ears.
'Look! A prisoner!' came the cry as he began to run.
To run as if his life on this depended,
For he was the prisoner.

And as he ran he thought,
And the thoughts brought forward tears of pain
Of misery and frustration that the months of capture
 had kept within him,
Had suppressed to save the tears of those who joined
 him in his fate.
A piercing scream was by a knot
Of bitterness held within his throat.
Adonai Elohenu – the Lord is our God,
And the sky grew dark and then darker still,
Adonai Ehad – the Lord is one.
One who tortured his followers and blessed the
 wrong.

It was as if he blessed the village boys who like their
  Nazi counterparts
Had shunned and spat and jostled.
The pillar of good intentions crumbled as they
  chanted 'Jew!'
And Rabbi Cohen lay on the ground.
Were they wrong or misinformed? Who was the
  outcast him or they?

Three men pursued, then two and one apart,
Then all three went their own ways.
Through the trees they ran whose fallen leaves
  rustled beneath their feet,
Colouring the damp earth a mixture of yellow ochre,
  red and burnt orange.
A fourth was running too—
The prisoner whose face was taut and pale with
  anxiety.
He remembered those who ventured to that factory
  over the hill.
Those who were joyful at the prospect of freedom
  but never returned,
But lay in a room beneath a heap of bodies;
Blank eyes staring.
Yisgaddal Veyiskaddah . . .
And the prisoner's pace quickened and his heart too
Sounding the execution call 'Jew! Jew!'
Yisgaddal Veyiskaddah Shemay Rabbah
A second appeared and a third and the scream that
  contorted his throat was free.

Surrounded.
And as they shot an image of each one appeared;
  freaks, outcasts, misfits themselves,
The deaf mute, the disfigured and the aged handicap
Who beat him down with his wooden stick.

Worse than any childlike nightmare was his death
As the bullets rocked his body to perform in gaudy
 spasms
While the mouth unspeaking betrayed agony
 unthought
And a single bloom of thorn apple fell in his hand.
High in the sky a brilliant star shot forward and hit the
 moon
And seemed to explode.
Silver fragments rained down and over the four a
 halo was suspended,
And the fragments fell in a six-point star around the
 dying man.
'Yom Kippur!' he cried with tears
As the radiance disintegrated and the flower
 crumbled.
Then they were transformed again and the Germans
 left him dead.

Hazel Aston (16)
(Highly commended)

The Queen Has Tooth Trouble

Newsflash,   bang
We are receiving reports   bang
        receiving reports   bang
        receiving reports,   bang
                                              bang
One,   bang
Two suspected dead,   bang
                Three.   bang
Four bombs,   bang
Audio images.   bang
Carnage.   Holocaust.   bang

```
                                    bang
they just stood there               bang
            stood there shouting     bang
    stood              shouting      bang
bastards, Bastards . . .   bastards.  bang
```

But,
Newsflashes aren't like that,
Newsflashes should break news
Gently,
Like soapsuds,
Gently,
Like warm blood,
Gently,
Transcending consciousness,
Not brutal,
It was too brutal,
Offending the sensibility.

this is the end of the newsflash

Eight people died,
And seven horses.

```
Police collected the four-inch
                   five-inch
                   six-inch
```
Nails,
Wrapped around the bombs.
Nails that penetrated,
Through the glass,
Through the mind,
Scarred your mind,
Cut you from your
Reality.
Back to earth
Below the earth.

Sullen putrefaction.

the IRA telephoned our Dublin office claiming
    responsiblity

A deeper cut,
Pouring salt into the nail wound.
Responsibility is a big world.
They are responsible
For making people see.

And shattering the peace.

The bandstand – Regent's Park
Will not be the same again.
the band were playing tunes from the popular
    musical Oliver

Six bandsmen were playing
Popular tunes.
They
Are as dead as

Everybody.

But they now see why.
Just the
Click . . . Click . . . Click . . .
As the needle grooves on endlessly.
The auto-reject has failed again,
And the bodies
Lie around,
Like paper cutouts
Blown over in a strong wind.

Kevin David Andrews (17)
(Highly commended)

Burying the Dead on Plumstead Common

On Plumstead Common where sewage gurgles from
    bursted pipes
Pits gape like sockets in the blanched and
    heat-bleached
Skulls stacked everywhere like trash; trees
Are jagged splints circled by black shapes shrieking
    and
Swooping for food; earth is cracked and the world is
    ringed
With the skull-like gape of shattered houses.

    The bloody glare of raging flames marks
        Greenwich
    From Plumstead curls the smell of smouldering
        flesh
    And from Woolwich the rumble of tumbling
        rubble.

A man with scabby brows and leprous face
Then covered his face against the reek of putrid meat.
He rests upon his spade which cut the pit
He spews upon (the pit that's prinked with bone
And stinking shredded flesh). He coughs again,
Then shovels dust on flesh and squealing rats.

    Once there was order:
    Which first fractured, then shattered:
    These fragments lacerate to handle:

The girl, a beauty, clambered over hunks of rubble
Down broken streets, past shattered walls
And the fizzling stems of lamp-posts.

The landscape is rocky and ugly, offers no place
To bolt from the two eager boys chasing down
Breathless rubble-ways till rubble confines her;
They grip her leg, smack and slap and clench her
To the leprous floor. She clamps her teeth, sees
The cracked-up town dissolving in a tear.

> The bubo bursts
> In greeny-red,
> The order lies
> Diseased and broke
> Where beauty lies
> Defiled and dead:
>> Fire and Plague
>> Fire and Plague
>> London has known before.
> The man who slops
> Along the bank
> Has salvaged bones
> From fetid mud
> But when he turns
> To cleanse his hand
> The River bursts:
> Fulvous, strong.

Belching black smoke the bonfires burn the
    wreckage:
Tyres smoulder with the reek of rubber,
The Marks and Spencer dresses sift to black ash
With the chipboard from the kitchen smeared with
    grease;
The bristles of a toothbrush curl, the plastic shoes
From Bata blister and liquify; a TV cracks and pops,
Hot splintered glass sinks into viscose suits as
Flames intensify over the cat's stiffened corpse,
Contort the tin cans, the brown and crinkled female

'Nuclear Bombed House', group work, Woodside County Primary School, Oswestry, Shropshire

Face; a silken stocking, lately stretched along
A silken leg, crimples and melts,
Dripping tears of nylon.

> I have salvaged what I could:
> I grabbed at shadows of fragments
> From a library whose books lay
> > luffing.

Here are my people: twisting from the shell of the
    town,
Not knowing where they are going, from where they
    come,
Not knowing the saw-tooth ruins of the town,
Dragging their clothes in tatters behind them
    dragging their
Flesh in tatters behind them, blistered faces
And bones above the skin, breaking sores and
    eyeballs
Scorched to pulp choking at the reek of their own
    burnt
Flesh choking at the taste of smoke and dust,
Wincing when they lick their sticky wounds
Sticky raw flesh wounds, shrieking when raw
Flesh sticks to earth which is scorched cracked earth
And does not yield screams of smarting pain
And the rumbling murmur of remorseful prayers

    'What can we salvage from these flames?'
      Fire and Plague, Fire and Plague . . .
    'What can be salvaged from the flame?'
      Fire and Plague, Fire and Plague . . .

   'These parting prayers, these ending prayers
Are all that we have left

      Amen.
      Amen.
      Amen.'

Mark Berry (17)
(Award winner)

Catalonia Streets
(For Arthur Koestler)

As the visible curtain
Of early evening curfew
Descends upon the volatile town,
Men in striped suits creep out
From clandestine political jails,
Through darkened streets
And silent alleys,
With the angel of blind motivation
Their only guide and stimulator.

Left behind are the unbroken shackles
And noiselessly-opened prison gates
Of writing pamphlets and stirring letters
In cold and sterile cells;
For now the simple, voluptuous words
Of ancient party slogans
Can be scrawled, letter by letter,
On the urine-dank walls
Of the dormant, unseeing town.

Stealing swiftly back
Once the deed is done
Past intimidation-shrouded town halls
And paint-daubed war memorials,
Searching for the names and numbers of contact
    addresses
That the monocled ex-party official in the room next
    door
Had slowly tapped out
Along the leaden pipes;
Searching in a hurried frenzy of after-curfew thought
For the reasons and ideals
Of the little red leaflet

Thrust into his eager hand
One distantly early on reveille.

Searching for infant memories
Of yellowing photographs
Of father on the estate,
Of serene, picture-portrait-prepared mother
With the serving girls,
Of uncle standing statuette-erect
In the linen factory,
Of elder brother in countlessly-medalled uniform;
Remembering all too well
The sudden flight and year-long wanderings
Through starving cities
And blighted lands,
Remembering seeing with puzzled, innocent eyes
The jewellery
On the pawn-shop counter
And in the smiling hands
Of the rough border sentry;
Remembering holding mother's hand
In the proletariat-stinking,
First-class refugee overflowing
Third-class railway carriage,
The salty cups of coffee
And suspicious leers of drunken foreign soldiers
In lonely, vodka'd railway cafés,
The jeering looks of refused beggars;
Remembering remembering with confused mind
How now-dead father had said
That just one signet ring
Would see them clear
For at least five years;
And how eventually the pale old man
Had squeezed his mystified hand
For the last and only time;

And wished him in mud-spatter'd,
Ypres lieutenant-general style
'God speed.'

Brought back from the halcyon daydream
By the siren-less wails
Of militia vehicles
And whispered shouts
Of as yet far-off figures;
Running anywhere, with convictions and
    action-courses
Spinning around a politic-less head,
Thinking only of immediate futures
And present survival.

Looking back in fifty years,
With tears and introspections
And guilt and smiles and signatures
And other momentary memories combining
To form the conscience complex.
Regal pictures of forgotten wedding days
Amid snaps of Claire and Yvonne and Pascal,
Successful books
And conclusive experiments;
The reminders of an ever-mutating life,
The knowledge that Los Endos cannot be far.

The hastily scribbled
'Don't go in.
Call the police'
Left for housemaid
And all and sundry
To see.

Duncan Marcus Heaster (15)
(Highly commended)

'Birds in a Storm', Richard Foster (7)

Drugs

The depression crept round,
Alerting her body of what was going to happen.
One, two, three she counted,
As she swallowed it,
Hoping it would cure her.

She stared in the mirror,
Waiting for a clearer,
More joyful picture.

Suddenly she felt an urge,
To leave the room,
To go down and rejoin the party,
To dance, to drink,
To die, to die, to die!
She fell into a deep daze. . . .

Emily Frances Garner (10)
(Highly commended)

Snow Sickness
(The snow stands both for the weather and for cocaine)

I hide behind the moving shadows
Of bluebirds on the wall,
Thread trailing from the empty eyes
Of needles.

Mirror reflections in empty bottles,
Butterfly colours,
Palette ready
To paint the day.
Crystal drops, so heavy
In my eyes
They hurt.
Heaven is Hell, from inside.

Dancing on cobwebs,
Dressing in gossamer.
Eating the sunbeams
Will keep me alive.
I ride on a bee's back,
Warm fuzzy stripes,
Black. White.
Beware the sting, if the driver is late.

Corridors of crystal,
Masked
In veils of mist.
Warm
In spite of the fairies' cold,
Jealous at my presence.
But, after all, it is a false passport,
And the customs will catch me soon.
Jam is sour
With this powder snow.

Sarah Childs (16)
(Highly commended)

In Pensive Mood

The Question of God?

God. A King? An Emperor? How do you define it?
A tired old man with the world at His feet?
A long white beard and a kind old face?
God, what do you think of your human race?
You invented it, so they say,
Do you regret it in any way?
What do you think of evil and sin,
And the world that I'm growing up in?
God, can you cry, can you weep?
Do you laugh? – or have nightmares in your sleep?
What do you do all day? How do you fill your time?
Or do you just invent another life – commit another
  crime?
Can't you see the sufferers everywhere,
Or are you short-sighted? Or don't you care?
Do you see the children and their eyes filled with
  moisture,
And their gawky faces and their awkward posture?
Do you see the mass murders and the world full of
  blood?
Or can't you see beyond the Church and its love?

'Archway in Winter', Deirdre MacDonald (14)

I can't understand you, God. It's your Creation,
Didn't you want a pure and gentle nation?
Didn't you want peace and tranquillity—
Or did you mean to have evil and impurity?

God! Are you there, listening to me?
Or am I just another voice, another silent plea?
Do you know what is happening on the land?
Can you see it from where you stand?

They're going to ruin your world, blow it all up.
Just one press on a button and the world will erupt.
You'll be out of a job, God. What will you do then?
Are you just going to begin all over again?

Rebecca Poole (15)

Not For Him

Not for Him a big white ambulance,
But a slow donkey.
Not for Him flashing blue lights,
But the star of Bethlehem.
Not for Him the white hospital wards,
But a cold stable.
Not for Him a nice warm cradle,
But a manger full of straw.
Not for Him fleecy babygros,
But plain swaddling bands.
Not for Him the Midwife, Nurse and Doctors,
But three simple shepherds.
Not for Him Auntie and Uncle from the North,
But three Kings from the East.
Not for Him a cuddly teddy bear,
But a shepherd boy's lamb.
Not for Him a silver coin in his palm,
But Frankincense, Myrrh and Gold.
Not for Him a future in computers,
But the crown of Heaven

Daniel Salcedo (11)
(Highly commended)

All Things

All things dark and fearful,
All humans big and strong,
All bombs loud and deadly;
Does the Lord God think it's wrong?

Each little flower that closes,
Each little bird that dies,
He made their fading colours,
That darken up the skies.

146

The purple-headed human,
With blood all running by,
The sunset and the morning,
That terrorise the sky.

He gave us guns to fight with
And arms to make our hell.
How great is God Almighty
Who has made all things well!

Lyndon Quinn (14)

A Short Meditation

Moonshadow night
Enormous night
Resting for the world,
Saying nothing.

Buddha night.

Sit and listen.
Listen to nothing
Hear your ears
Listening,
Deafened.

Ben Charles Miles (15)

Life

A box with precise measurements
Cut right
Right proportion
The same type and shade of wood
No knots
Varnished in pure wood varnish
Why?

A person who never sins
Never gets a question wrong
Always tells the truth
Never needs to be told off
Never inflicts pain on others
Who?

A village small and symmetrical
Neat thatched cottages
An inn
A village church
No pollution
Or violence
Where?

A small perfect organism
No faults
Uniform in colour
Cells ageless
Lives forever
What?

We aren't all quite right.
None of us fits the jigsaw
Of the world quite correctly.

Gerard Day (12)

'Main Gate', Lorraine Bryan (15)

The Silver Rain

The Silver Rain
The Shining Sun
The fields where scarlet poppies run
And all the ripples of the wheat
Are in the bread that I do eat
And when I sit for every meal
And say a grace I always feel
That I am eating rain and sun
The fields where scarlet poppies run

> Yasmin Isaacs (10)
> (Highly commended)

Pictures From An Exhibition

When I was small,
I was in love,
With everything.
Everything swam with vivid colours
And was bathed in a beautiful light
With huge size and scope
Everything was new.

The fragile blue of a Sunday sky,
Sunday sounds of children
Drowned by the warm distance.
Billowing clouds of broken hymns
Drift lazily in their own time
From the warehouse brick chapel,
Swirling across the empty gardens,
And I'm with my own friends
Running alone around somewhere else
Getting my heavy slippers soaked with dew
And next door's girl quietly watches me
For hour and hours and. . . .

I remember how beautiful water was to me,
Dancing in cool curves through itself,
Making moving dark patches on the
Flickering bottom of the tank,
Throwing a wavy sun back into my eyes,
Blinding my mother with my smiles . . .
But now it's ice, and my eyes, like ice,
Don't see.

Sometimes . . .
I used to play all day
Through thick summer smells
Of fresh-cut grass,
Green holiday afternoons,

With soft backlit paper skies
With my bony wire friend
Who was all elbows and knees
And who was so different
To me . . .
When the soft warming sun sank,
Like a big purple egg,
Into a dust-reddened dusk
And a mother would call
From a long way away
Across chimneys of green
And slippery grass
　　　　To stop
　　　　And kill the day for good.
Gone
All gone
I used to say
The green is dead
Gone
All gone
All gone grey.

Stuart Williams (15)
(Highly commended)

A Song

Here on the wind
Crawling from far away
Lost in the night
Wandering through the day
Voices from the park
Searching from far away
Lost in the night
Wandering through the day.

Diksha Unjia (6)
(Highly commended)

'Portrait of Myself', Iain Kirkpatrick (9)

Uncle John's Paintbox

One day
　He came to say,
Would you like to see,
　My paintbox,
And this is what he told me.

Black is a burglar running into the night,
A hidden lucky cat;
Or coal about to light,
The hidden mysteries in your mind.

Brown appears as trees bowing in an Autumn wind,
Or newly made hot buttered toast,
Melting chocolate by the fire,
An escaping fox.

Green is the harvest fields,
Or new spring grass,
Dense African jungle
Or a parrot's tail.

Blue might be a pool, deep and cool,
Or the cold around your feet,
The sea, angry and restless,
Or a clear sky on a summer day.

Red could be blood oozing out of a cut,
Flames dancing in the fire,
Or a juicy apple about to fall,
The scene after the Glencoe massacre.

Silver could be tears streaming the face,
Dew on the morning grass,
Or hail hitting the fragile window pane,
A crown upon a prince's head.

Gold is the harvest moon, sun of night,
Treasure deep below,
Or coins gleaming in the golden light,
Ripe wheat shivering in the cold wind.

Yellow is the street lights at night,
Or a flickering candle light,
Bananas hanging high above,
Lion's teeth glistening in the sunlight.

White might be a tiger's whiskers,
Ashes of a dying fire,
Ghosts on a nightly haunt,
Or rooftops in winter.

Kevin O'Dowda (11)
(Highly commended)

What is White?

White is the steam which comes from a kettle,
White is the flower on the stinging nettle.
White is the swan gliding down the stream,
White are the stars and the pale moonbeams.
White are the clouds which float in the sky,
White are the doves which fly on high.
White is the magic which of course is good,
White is the snowman in our garden he stood.
White is the icing on the Christmas cake,
White is the colour of a soft snowflake.
White is a lady's wedding dress,
White are some of the pieces in a game of chess.
White are the lies we sometimes tell,
White is your face when you're not very well
White is the sherbert in a sherbert fountain,
White is the top of a snow-capped mountain.
White is a baby's christening robe,
White are the countries on the top and bottom of the
    globe.
White are the ghosties which give us a fright,
Can you imagine living without white?

Sara Peacock (10)

Black

Which is stronger? Light or dark?
Pick now or forever battle with
The slim dark stranger in your eye
And the fat white person in your voice.
See chalk fly across your classroom board,
Or the ink pen across the page.
Light and dark:
But which one wins?
A coloured boy hoping for a friend
Then looming shadows
Of light figures blanking out hope.
You choose white.
But you are wrong!
Black. Black is strong.

Tracey Elizabeth Hales (13)
(Highly commended)

What is Brown?

Eyes are brown,
And I think
A frown is brown.
Bats in a cave
And pennies I save.
The tufted thread
On the cover of a bed.
Plant pots
And granny knots.
Knitting wools
And wooden stools.

Catherine Welsh (7)

Index of titles

Index of authors

More Beaver Books

We hope you have enjoyed this book. Here are some of the other poetry titles published by Beaver Books:

Poems For Fun A Beaver original. An ideal introduction to verse for younger readers, packed with poems about all kinds of fun – games, parties, puzzles, even school. Compiled by Zenka and Ian Woodward and illustrated throughout by Tony Escott

The Beaver Book of Animal Verse A Beaver original. A beautiful collection of poetry about all kinds of animals, compiled by Raymond Wilson, with superb line drawings by Tessa Barwick

The Beaver Book of Skool Verse A Beaver original. An amazing collection of poems and verses about school, including playground rhymes and games, mnemonics, verses about school dinners, lessons, teachers, end of term and exams. Lots of the material came from children all over the country who sent in their favourite rhymes, and the collection was put together by Jennifer Curry, with cartoons by Graham Thompson

These and many other Beavers are available from your local bookshop or newsagent, or can be ordered direct from: Hamlyn Paperback Cash Sales, PO Box 11, Falmouth, Cornwall TR10 9EN. Send a cheque or postal order made payable to the Hamlyn Publishing Group, for the price of the book plus postage at the following rates:
UK: 45p for the first book, 20p for the second book, and 14p for each additional book ordered to a maximum charge of £1.63;
BFPO and Eire: 45p for the first book, 20p for the second book, plus 14p per copy for the next 7 books and thereafter 8p per book;
OVERSEAS: 75p for the first book and 21p for each extra book.

New Beavers are published every month and if you would like the *Beaver Bulletin*, a newsletter which tells you about new books and gives a complete list of titles and prices, send a large stamped addressed envelope to:

Beaver Bulletin
The Hamlyn Group
Astronaut House
Feltham
Middlesex TW14 9AR

207773